C000242570

CHRISTIE'S
COLLECTABLES

Contents

PRICE CODES

The following price codes are used in this book:
£A Less than £150 **£B** £151–£400
£C £401–£800 **£D** £801–£2,500 **£E** £2,501–£7,500
£F £7,501–£15,000 **£G** More than £15,000

Valuation is an imprecise art and prices can vary for many
reasons, including the condition of a piece, fashion and national and
regional interest. Prices given in this book are approximate
and based on likely *auction* values. *Insurance* values reflect the
retail replacement price and as such are liable to be higher.

Introduction

STAFFORDSHIRE FIGURES ARE AMONG THE MOST EASILY recognizable artefacts in British ceramics. Potters first made them early in the 18th century and continued until World War II, and some are reproduced to this day. They are as cherished now as they were in the 19th century. At the time, they were popular because they were cheap alternatives to the expensive and prestigious models made for the rich by the great porcelain manufacturers. Today, they are collected across the world, including in the United States, because they represent a slice of history and the charm of a bygone era.

Although the work is largely perceived as models of people and, of course, the ubiquitous dogs, Staffordshire

Kilns for firing pottery, like those used in Staffordshire, are shown in this 1831 illustration by G.S. Shepherd.

This delicate Meissen figure of Columbine from c.1744 is an example of the expensive porcelain figures appreciated by the elite.

potters made a huge range of wares, including ordinary household items such as plates, jugs and tea services. Staffordshire figures are seen as a generic type, since it is rare to attribute particular pieces to individual potters. Although they were hand finished and painted, the majority of figures were made from moulds, and so the level of individuality is reduced. Nonetheless, the inherent fragility of any ceramic artefact makes many pieces rare; it is their rarity and the fascinating range of subject matter that make most pieces endearing and collectable.

𝒯he subject matter of Staffordshire figures has changed during the history of the genre, resulting in an immense range of pieces. Early pieces are often concerned with rural or classical themes. It was later, from the 1840s onward, that portrait figures celebrating great events in contemporary public life became prevalent. This may have been connected to Queen Victoria's ascension to the throne and the expansion of the British Empire, along with the changing political scene in Europe. Today's equivalents would probably include models of the Prince of Wales, John Major, President Clinton and Chancellor Kohl. It was not only statesmen, military heroes and monarchs that appealed to the potters and the public; huge numbers of models depicting theatrical

A ballad sheet from c.1827 by H.G. Maguire for the song Buy Image! *shows a street vendor selling figures.*

and notorious personalities were made as well. The theatrical groups were often copied from printed material advertising the production, and the figures were sold outside the theatre. A smaller number of figures were of criminals and crime scenes. Pastille-burners, often modelled as houses, were also created – poor sanitation in the mid-19th century made such items essential to any city household.

The earliest figures are now rare and prices dictate that the ordinary collector will be unlikely to obtain such pieces as "Polito's Menagerie" (see p.34) or a saltglaze bear jug (see p.13). By their very nature, fewer of these pieces have survived. Subsequent developments in pottery techniques have created more substantial and long-lasting wares. For example, the use of moulds with hardly any – or no – applied pieces that could be broken off made later pieces less susceptible to accidents. Naturally, age is a factor; early pieces have had to survive intact longer than mid-19th century items.

$\mathcal{C}$omplicated early pieces with several figures and intricate details were made by hand from sheets and strips of clay and built up in gradual stages. Single figures of animals from the late 18th century were sometimes made by "slip moulding"; liquid clay, or slip, was poured into ready-made single plaster moulds. Before firing, extra appendages, made by hand, were added to the form to give the figures a three-dimensional appearance. By the mid-19th century, the "flatback" figures were almost entirely made from a mould in two parts. Sheets of clay were pressed into each side of the mould, which was then drawn together; the pieces squeezed outside were cut off, leaving a ridge, or mould line. These moulds were used several hundred times until the features became indistinct.

$\mathcal{D}$ecorating techniques also evolved. Early pieces were fired, then sparingly decorated in simple coloured glazes and given a "glaze firing", that is, a second firing to fix

The evangelist Dwight Lynam Moody was made in this press mould from the Samson Smith factory.

the glaze. The later pieces were given the initial "biscuit" firing, followed by a clear glaze firing, and only then were painted with bright overglaze enamels, which were fired yet another time. Overglaze enamel decoration used ground glass within a medium of oil, which burned off during the firing process. These paints were applied in stages, because certain colours fix at different temperatures. Although the mid-19th century figures used almost entirely overglaze enamels, sometimes one of the firings was omitted as a way of saving on cost: the piece was coloured by using cobalt (blue) or manganese (purple), which could be painted on after the biscuit firing and fired under the clear glaze.

Although it is often difficult to ascertain which factory a figure came from, there are exceptions. Such makers as Obadiah Sherratt, Thomas Whieldon, the Wood family and others have distinctive identifying factors – perhaps their style, a written record or a mark. The Wood family were probably the first to use a mark – the family name impressed into the body. Sherratt's work is also easy to attribute: it is well recorded and his subject matter is peculiar to his factory. Other potters copied successful wares made by the more original and better known factories.

Staffordshire potters made practical wares, such as this tea canister from c.1785, with King George III in relief.

This 1860 group of the two Cushman sisters in the roles of Romeo and Juliet was modelled on a playbill.

TIPS FOR COLLECTORS

• Buy figures you like and can afford. Don't let others pressurize you into buying pieces for your collection.

• Avoid common 19th-century figures with restoration. With diligence, you should find an almost perfect piece. Many early pieces have damage, however; restoration may be unavoidable. Restoration is measured by quality: some pieces are lovingly restored but others are rough.

• Clean pieces with care: heavy scrubbing can damage overglaze enamels. Occasional gentle cleaning in mild soapy lukewarm water is sufficient. Because restoration work has not been fired, do not wash restored pieces.

• Try to buy from specialists or reputable auction houses, who can guide you in your purchases and look for pieces you would like to augment your collection.

• Nobody wants a fake in their collection. If you don't know what you are looking for, ask someone who does. Modern reproductions use a different pottery body and the glaze is overly crazed to give an appearance of age.

Pew group

THIS GROUP IS AMONG THE EARLIEST RECOGNIZED
figure groups from the Staffordshire potters.
It is a typical "pew group" from c.1745, so called
because of the way in which the figures are
seated on a pew. It is difficult to say exactly how
many survive – perhaps as few as 10. They
are so sought after by wealthy collectors
that the pieces circulate among them and come
up at auction more often than might be
expected – but this is still infrequent.
THIS PEW GROUP IS MADE FROM SALTGLAZE POTTERY.
Handfuls of salt were thrown into the kiln during
the firing process. The salt vaporized and formed
a glaze on the surface, which has a rough,
colourless texture. In contrast to the majority of
19th-century figures, these groups are predominantly
made by modelling pieces of clay by hand.
Height 6¼in/16cm   £G

Saltglaze bear jug

THE EXTRUDED CLAY FUR ON THIS FIGURE MAKES IT
*appear quite different from the pew group
(see opposite), but it is another example of saltglaze.
At first glance it may be assumed that the bear is
an ornamental piece, but it was designed as a jug –
the head comes off to function as a lid and drinking
cup. The sparse decoration is limited to brown
glaze to highlight the eyes, paws and collar.*
AS REFLECTED IN ITS VALUE, THIS IS ONE OF THE EARLIER
*types of bear-baiting jugs, made c.1750. Such
jugs were manufactured, however, in a variety of
styles and bodies well into the 19th century.
This reflects the fact that bear-baiting was a
popular sport for many years, being outlawed only
in 1835. The dog visible between the bear's
front legs is a common feature that illustrates
the role of baiting dogs in the sport.*
Height 10½in/26.5cm £F

Whieldon owl jug

THOMAS WHIELDON WAS FIRST APPRENTICED TO
*John Astbury, one of the original known potters of
Staffordshire who made basic moulded figures
decorated with simple coloured glazes. By 1740,
Whieldon had his own family-run works in Fenton
Low, producing wares similar to those made by
Astbury. They both used coloured glazes that were
produced by firing metal oxides into the glaze, rather
than over-painting with coloured enamels.*

MODELLED ON A NATURALISTIC FORM, THIS OWL JUG, DATING
*from c.1760, has a removable head that serves
as a lid. The mottled glazes are typically attributed
to Thomas Whieldon, but not all such products
were made by this single family of potters.*

Height 6in/15cm £G

Such details as the eyebrows,
feathers and wings were
made by applying strips of
moulded clay to the body.

Arbour group

*T*HIS ARBOUR GROUP, FROM C.*1765*, IS MADE
*of a cream-coloured earthenware known as
creamware. By the mid-18th century, English
porcelain manufacturers, such as Chelsea and Bow,
were producing a variety of figures that were
influenced by Oriental and Continental
designs. Some enterprising Staffordshire potters,
including John Astbury, filled a gap in the
market by using less expensive creamware to
make figures in a porcelain style.*
*T*HE TWO WOMEN IN THE ARBOUR WERE PRESS-MOULDED;
*the arbour itself was probably modelled by
hand. The piece is coloured with yellow, green
and brown glazes. These groups are extremely
rare, particularly ones that feature two
women. Most single figures are of men,
for example musicians and soldiers.*
Height 5in/13cm   £G

Pratt-type group

MADE OF A BUFF-COLOURED POTTERY BODY, THIS
*group of a cow, calf and milkmaid is known as a
Pratt type, after the family of potters who worked in
Lane Delft, in the Potteries area in Staffordshire.
Although this particular group is thought to
have been made in Yorkshire c.1800–20, rather than
Staffordshire, the Pratt name is used generically
to indicate this type of coloured decoration. It was
not uncommon for potters around the country to
take their inspiration from the popular pieces
emanating from Staffordshire, which was the largest
area of pottery production in Great Britain.*

THE BASE HAS AN INTERESTING SPONGE PATTERN AND THE
*figure itself has unusual colour schemes (the purple
patches on the body of the cow, for example). This
group was popular into the late 19th century,
although the body and style changed by the 1850s.*

Height 6in/15cm   £D

Pratt-type plaques

*T*HESE PLAQUES HAVE DISTINCTIVE *P*RATT-TYPE
*coloured glazes decorating creamware or pearlware
pottery bodies. They illustrate the late 18th- to early
19th-century taste for classical subjects, including
(clockwise from top left): a woman, perhaps Sorrow;
a woman with a winged putto, possibly Venus
and Cupid; a woman holding grapes – she may be
Ariadne; Prometheus chained to a rock and
being attacked by an eagle; and a moulded muse
among acanthus-leaf decoration.*

*T*HE MUSE HAS A PEARLWARE BODY, SO CALLED BECAUSE OF
*the colour of its glaze, which was intended to imitate
porcelain and became more popular than creamware
(the other plaques are creamware). Pearlware is
produced by adding a small amount of cobalt to the
glaze to give it a bluish, porcellaneous effect.*

Height Ariadne 8in/20cm £B each

Creamware figures

*P*RATT-TYPE GLAZES WERE APPLIED TO THESE *creamware figures, dating from the late 18th to early 19th centuries. Because they were easily and inexpensively produced, figures such as these were made in vast quantities, and many have survived because they are robust. They were made by a process known as slip moulding, whereby slip, or liquid clay, was poured into a ready-made mould, which could be used many times.*

*F*IGURES REPRESENTING THE SEASONS WERE POPULAR. *The boy holding a basket of flowers might represent summer or autumn. It is not clear whether the woman holding a bundle represents any particular season or is merely intended to illustrate rural pastimes.*

Height woman 5½in/14cm   £A

Pearlware classical figures

*T*HESE CLASSICAL FIGURES PORTRAY, FROM LEFT
*to right, Cleopatra; a woman who is probably
emblematic of Love; a woman who may be Hygeia,
the goddess of health; and a figure representing
Fortitude. These pieces, made c.1800–20, are
typical of the execution of historical and
mythological figures by various Staffordshire
potters. Less typical, is the substantial size of the
two centre examples, which have become
increasingly more difficult to find.*

*T*HE SMALLER FIGURES OF CLEOPATRA AND FORTITUDE,
*which are representative of the Ralph Wood type,
are about 8in/20cm high. If in reasonable condition
and not produced by an identifiable potter,
they are worth about a tenth of the value of their
larger counterparts. The smaller figures, however,
are more likely to be available at auction.*

Height Love 29½in/75cm £D

Pearlware cockerel

FIGURES OF FARM ANIMALS AND BIRDS WERE popular into the mid-19th century. Gambling on cock fighting, a prevalent sport, was a favourite pastime of many people. From the mid-18th century, many of these figures were painted with a combination of coloured glazes. This late 18th- to early 19th-century cockerel, however, was painted with enamels over a pearl glaze.

COLOURED ENAMELS NEED A GREAT DEGREE OF KNOWLEDGE to produce and apply them properly. Enamels are frit, or glass-based, paints which produce their colours upon firing. Pieces decorated with enamels require more firings than those with glazes, making them more costly. Despite this, the more brilliant enamels soon replaced the glazes.

Height 3¾in/9.5cm £B

Wood-type Neptune

THE **W**OODS WERE A LARGE FAMILY *of potters working in Burslem at the end of the 18th century and had various partnerships between them. It is difficult to know precisely whether unmarked pieces, such as the ones here, were made by them, or by other potters who simply copied their work or who were in partnership with them. Some basic marks were used (probably by Ralph Wood II and III) and took the form of their names impressed in the body: "Ra. Wood Burslem." These marked pieces clearly identify the type of work manufactured by the Wood family; other pieces that are similar are known generically as Wood-type.*

NEPTUNE WAS A POPULAR CLASSICAL *subject. These figures represent two ways the subject was handled at different periods: a pearlware Wood-type bust from the late 18th century and a creamware Wood-type Neptune standing on a dolphin, from the early 19th century.*

Height bust 11½in/29cm   £B–C

Height figure 11in/28cm   £B

Wood-type Toby jug

THE ORIGIN OF THE TOBY JUG IS UNKNOWN, BUT
it is one of the most recognizable and enduring of
Staffordshire products. Some have suggested that
Toby was the hero Uncle Toby of Laurence Sterne's
book Tristram Shandy, *but others believe that*
he may have been a character by the name of Toby
Philpot, a celebrated Yorkshire drinker.
THIS LATE 18TH-CENTURY WOOD-TYPE JUG WAS MODELLED
in a typical seated pose, with the man holding
a mug of foaming ale. Tobies come in many shapes
and sizes and in characters other than Uncle Toby,
including World War I generals. The Toby featured
here is slightly less common than most Wood-type
examples. More common pearlware Toby jugs
are worth half its value at auction; rarer types, such
as Martha Gunn, could be worth double.
Height 10in/25cm £C

Figure of Chaucer

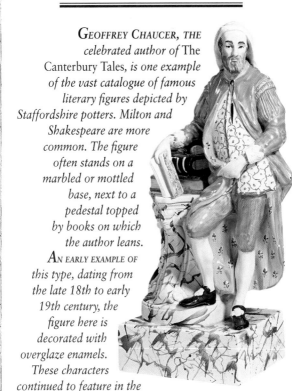

Geoffrey Chaucer, the *celebrated author of* The Canterbury Tales, *is one example of the vast catalogue of famous literary figures depicted by Staffordshire potters. Milton and Shakespeare are more common. The figure often stands on a marbled or mottled base, next to a pedestal topped by books on which the author leans.*

An early example of *this type, dating from the late 18th to early 19th century, the figure here is decorated with overglaze enamels. These characters continued to feature in the more readily available flatback figures of the mid-19th century. The Derby porcelain factory produced similar pedestal-type figures at the time and may be where the inspiration came from.*

Height 12½in/31.5cm £C

On the pedestal, under the book in Chaucer's hand, is a delicately shaped face. Another detail is the painted flowers on the inside of the coat.

Vicar & Moses

Vicar & Moses

ONE OF THE MOST AMUSING STAFFORDSHIRE
*subjects, this group from c.1800 is an unusual one,
showing an inebriated vicar being helped home
by his clerk, Moses. (A reproduction version of this
group is shown on page 77.) More common
examples show the vicar asleep in a pulpit and
Moses attempting to wake him; these fetch half the
price of the one here at auction.*

THE GROUP HAS BEEN ATTRIBUTED TO ENOCH WOOD,
*who was a later member of the large Wood family
of potters of Burslem. Enoch moved away
from the family's earlier styles. His modelling
often demonstrated greater clarity
and definition, perhaps because in his youth
he studied under his uncle William Caddick,
a painter in Liverpool.*

Height 11½in/29cm £C

Bocage with St. Peter

PETER

THIS 1820–30 PEARLWARE FIGURE OF ST. PETER IS
completely painted in overglazed enamels. St. Peter
is kneeling in prayer, with a cockerel and the Gospel
of St. Mark beside him. The raised pad on the
front of the base, with the words "St Peter", is not
unusual but neither is it the norm. Painted titles
became fashionable by the mid-19th century.

LITTLE IS LEFT OF THE FOLIAGE, BUT WHAT IS THERE IS A GOOD
example of a bocage. The term refers to the foliate
sprig decoration and tree that often accompany
such models. It was popular with porcelain
manufacturers because it provided a way to support
figures that might otherwise sag in the kiln during
firing. Because of the nature of pottery figures,
the risk of sagging is not as marked – the bocage
has a purely decorative function.

Height 8½in/21.5cm   £B

Walton bocage group

THIS "TENDERNESS" GROUP of a shepherd and a girl standing before a flowering bocage, with a sheep in the foreground, was made c.1825. It was made in several parts: the figures, the sheep, the foliage of the bocage and the base were all separately moulded, then applied as a whole. It is a good example of pottery from the Walton school, which often made figures with people or animals in front of a bocage. This model has a genuine mark, making it attributable to John Walton.

WALTON WORKED IN BURSLEM FROM THE LATE 18TH TO early 19th centuries, but there are a number of other manufacturers who made similar wares. Identification is only possible when the potters, such as the Salt and Tittensor families, mark their pieces. Some later reproductions carry the scroll mark, so care must be taken to examine the body, colouring and style before confirming attribution.

Height 7¾in/20cm   £C

A scroll mark stamped "Walton" at the back of the figure identifies John Walton as the maker.

Bocage with a doe

A DOE STANDING BEFORE A FLOWERING BOCAGE
*is the subject of this pearlware model, painted
with enamels, from c.1820. Deer were a popular
subject, as suggested by the many surviving
examples; this may have been because they had
sporting significance or for purely sentimental
reasons. Sheep were also a favourite.*

*S*OMETIMES THE SUBJECT APPEARS NOT AS A PURELY
*decorative bocage group but as a spill vase,
frequently as a pair consisting of a stag and doe.
It is likely that this model was once part of
such a pair, and it would be reasonably easy to find a
matched mate. These naive bocage groups, with
their extensive enamel decoration, must
have been reasonably expensive to produce – but
still cheaper than a porcelain equivalent.*

Height 6½in/16.5cm £B

Bird spill

*T*HIS UNUSUALLY ELABORATE, BUT COMPARATIVELY
*inexpensive, group from c.1810 depicts a pair
of birds perched beside an egg-filled nest in a tree,
with a group of sheep in front. It would be
more typical to have either the birds or the
sheep alone. Similar bird spills continued to
be made into the mid-19th century.*

A SPILL VASE IS USUALLY MODELLED WITH THE TRUNK
*of a tree, or another similarly shaped object,
functioning as the holder of wooden spills (used
for lighting candles, pipes and the like, much
as a match is used). Due to their ornate nature,
these spills were probably given as presents
to a smoking companion or were purchased as
a decorative item to sit on a mantelpiece.*

Height 6in/15cm   £B

Pearlware tiger group

PAINTED WITH OVERGLAZED ENAMELS, THIS
*large pearlware group is of a tiger on a stepped
base attacking a deer. Although it is similar
to other tiger groups made in the early 19th
century by Obadiah Sherratt, the potter
usually used a style of base that more closely
resembles a table. The tiger and deer group is not
very common – more typically, the tiger is
attacking an Indian army officer in a group
known as "The Death of Munroe".*
A CLOSE EXAMINATION OF THE PIECE WILL REVEAL HOW
*relatively easy it would be to change the group,
substituting the deer for Lieutenant Munroe or
vice versa. The deer itself is a separate piece
from the tiger and the base. This particular design
is illustrative of the versatile nature of many
Staffordshire figures. During this period,
the process of creating the groups might include
both moulding and modelling by hand.*
Length 14½in/37cm £F

The Dandies

THE PEARLWARE GROUP known as "The Dandies" could have been made by a number of Staffordshire manufacturers, including Obadiah Sherratt. This example is unlikely to be by Sherratt, however, since the figures are standing on a square base with no adornment. Indeed, it is Sherratt's bases that make much of his work recognizable. Sherratt's rendering of the group typically has a rocky moulded base with elaborate scrolls to the front.

WHOEVER THE MANUFACTURER, ALL THE FIGURES ARE similar. They show a man and woman fashionably dressed, strolling arm-in-arm. In the 1820s, the elaborate fashions of the day must have appeared somewhat amusing to many people and these figures may have been a humorous pastiche commenting on London vanity. It is likely that "The Dandies" was only in production for about 10 years or so; however, it still appears at auction a few times a year.

Height 8in/20cm £C

Pearlware camels

THESE PEARLWARE SPILL VASES, DESIGNED TO FACE
each other, are modelled after two types of camel:
the bactrian and the dromedary. As this is an
unusual subject for Staffordshire manufacturers,
especially in 1825–30 when they were made, these
figures are more valuable than those of similar
quality of commonplace European animals.

ALTHOUGH THE CAMELS ARE FULLY PAINTED IN OVERGLAZE
enamels, in shades of brown for the body and green
for the base, they are drab in comparison to
other figures with an enamel finish. The modeller,
however, paid attention to detail – the hair, for
example, was incised by hand. He must have studied
a contemporary engraving because the rendering
of the camels is not nearly as naive or fanciful
as some other exotic animals, such as lions
and tigers, which were probably produced in the
late 1700s. It has been noted that in 1810, a
camel, the property of Gilbert Pidcock, was sold
as "the only one alive in England".

Length 6in/15cm   £E

Sherratt bull-baiting group

OBADIAH SHERRATT WAS A PROLIFIC POTTER
*who worked in the Burslem area in the early 19th
century. He produced a wide range of subjects,
and his observation and sense of the
macabre have made him a favourite Staffordshire
potter among many collectors.*

THIS CREAM-COLOURED POTTERY GROUP, MADE
*c.1820–30, is a study of bull baiting. It depicts a
chained bull tossing a terrier over one shoulder
while another terrier bites the bull's nose.
At the bull's hindquarters a man, known as Captain
Lad, stands with his arms raised. Two oval
pads, inscribed "Bull Beating" and "Now Captin
Lad" (sic), were applied on the base.*

IN THIS, THE LARGER OF TWO GROUPS THAT SHERRATT
*produced on the subject, the figures stand
on a table base – suitable for supporting such
a heavy body. This type of base was
typically associated with Sherratt's work.*

Length 15¾in/40cm £1,500–£2,000

Sherratt Red Barn group

BASED ON A MURDER THAT WAS A CELEBRATED NEWS story in 1827, "The Red Barn" group (1828–30) is an example of Sherratt's interest in topical subjects that gripped the public imagination. William Corder shot, stabbed and strangled Maria Marten and buried her under the floor of a barn. When Maria's body was found and Corder was arrested, he said that she had committed suicide – clearly a risible story – but he finally confessed and was hanged shortly afterward. This case, with its elements of sex, violence and wickedness, inspired a play, which, although it used a degree of artistic licence, remained popular for many years.

THIS IS A KNOWN SHERRATT PIECE: IT HAS HIS FAMILIAR table base and his bocage is slightly different from the bocages of other manufacturers. Eventually, more pieces might be attributable to other potters through the study of variations in the leaves and flowers on bocages.

Length 11in/28cm   £3,000–£4,000

Polito's Menagerie

In 1808 THE CIRCUS VISITED WOLVERHAMPTON,
*not far from Burslem where Sherratt was based. It is
likely that Sherratt saw the circus, or a poster for it,
and was inspired to create "Polito's Menagerie"
(c.1825–35). Inscribed on the piece are the words:
"Politos menagerie of the wonderfull burds
and beasts from most part of the world: Lion&C"
(sic). Wombwell, another circus owner, succeeded
Polito, and later groups may be of his menagerie.*
MANY CONSIDER THIS GROUP TO BE SHERRATT'S MASTERPIECE.
*It was technically a difficult piece to fire, due to the
size of the base and the applied figures (separately
modelled and attached to the base), which
might all have had different rates of shrinkage. It is
painted in overglaze enamels, which would
have required different firing temperatures for some
colours. The group is possibly earlier than the
date suggested, since Polito died in 1814.*

Width 13¾in/35cm £F

Bust of Maria Foote

MARIA FOOTE WAS A FAMOUS AND talented actress on the West End stage in the 19th century. She also toured extensively. It was her notorious private life, however, which made her an appealing subject for Sherratt. She had many lovers and two illegitimate children. When an engagement was broken off, Maria won a breach of promise action and was awarded £3,000 as compensation – a huge amount of money at the time. Maria retired from the stage in 1831 and married the Earl of Harrington.

THE BUST OF MARIA FOOTE, MADE C.1816, IS TYPICAL of bust figures of the period. This one is easily identifiable as a Sherratt creation because it rests on one of his characteristic table bases. Most other manufacturers used a socle, or pedestal, base. All the busts were painted in a similar fashion, with bright enamels. The high value of this relatively simple piece reflects Sherratt's popularity among modern collectors and the comparative rarity of this subject.

Height 11½in/29cm £D

Various animals

ANIMALS WERE FAVOURED BY MANY POTTERS
in the last quarter of the 18th century. This typical
selection includes a Yorkshire pearlware cow
creamer and cover (above centre), a pair
of Ralph Wood-type creamware models of
a stag and hind (above left and right) and a
pair of pearlware models of a ewe and ram,
possibly from Yorkshire (below).

COMPARATIVELY EASY PIECES TO MANUFACTURE, THESE
figures were moulded and decorated with
coloured glazes. Presumably, along with the
relatively simple moulded figures of people, animals
such as these would have been the mainstay
of the average Staffordshire potter of the period.
The cow creamer and cover are valued at the
lower end of
the price range;
the other
figures are at the
upper end of
the range.

Length Cow creamer
6½in/16.5cm £D–E

Pearlware lion

LIONS ARE ALWAYS A POPULAR SUBJECT WITH
*collectors and, indeed, appear to have been popular
when they were first made – there are many types
and styles produced by a variety of potters.*
THIS EARLY 19TH-CENTURY PEARLWARE LION STANDS ON
*an oval stepped base, playfully resting a forepaw
on a yellow ball with black dots. The figure was
decorated in overglaze enamel. Although it
was influenced by the famous Florentine
Medici lions, this model is a comparatively naive
rendering of the subject – even for Staffordshire
pieces. Generally, the lions have greater
definition than this one does, particularly
pearlware examples from the late 18th century.
The lions were usually manufactured in pairs,
like the original Medici lions.*

Length 6¼in/16cm £D

Lloyd of Shelton-type lions

THESE LLOYD OF SHELTON-TYPE LIONS HAVE extruded clay manes and are modelled recumbent, with lambs in the foreground. Dating from c.1840, the figures are representative of lions in a biblical context. By the mid-19th century, most figures appear to have some gilding, however little. In comparison, considerable gilding was used on these examples to outline and decorate the bases and to highlight small features on the lions. Along with this more liberal use of gilding, the pottery body itself changed; it has a more porcellaneous nature.

JOHN AND REBECCA LLOYD WERE KNOWN TO BE working in Shelton from 1834 to 1852. They produced several figures and groups, not only in earthenware but also in porcelain, possibly reflecting the fact that the technical difficulties in making porcelain in Great Britain in the 18th century had been overcome. Occasionally, some of their pieces are impressed with the mark "Lloyd Shelton". The potters Wood and Caldwell also made pearlware models of these lions.

Length 4¾in/12cm   £D

Lion & tiger groups

The porcelain tiger and serpent spill vase group (left) was probably made c.1835–40 by Samuel Alcock, who produced a wide variety of animals in porcelain. The Alcock factories, at Corbridge and Burslem, produced an extensive range of items, including parian figures and tea wares, and some of them carry factory marks and pattern numbers. These animal figures are more difficult to attribute directly, but some have been known to carry a small incised model number.

Height 6¼in/16cm £D

Thomas Parr was one of a group of potters bearing this name, who worked at Church Street, Burslem, from 1852 to 1870. Various partnerships can be traced from here to the William Kent Ltd. factory of the 20th century. The group of the lion and tiger (right) is a Thomas Parr type, from c.1860. Kent and Parr-type pieces are noted for their pale enamels and the porcellaneous nature of the body.

Height 8¼in/21cm £D–E

Dogs & children

THE CHILDREN IN THIS PORCELAIN PAIR, DATING *from c.1840, are seated on recumbent setters with liver spots. The figures are set on gilt-line bases, with the girls and dogs in slightly different positions. Unlike the majority of groups, these were made of porcelain, the favoured medium for manufacturers such as Samuel Alcock and the Rockingham factory in Yorkshire. Another unusual feature is the rectangular bases – most mid-19th century animal groups from Staffordshire are on oval bases. These figures were modelled by hand and by using moulds, and they were decorated with overglaze enamel colours.*

THERE ARE MANY MID-19TH CENTURY VERSIONS OF *children and dogs, some of which are thought to be of the Prince of Wales and the Princess Royal. These groups are more endearing to collectors than the figures of dogs alone, so they usually command a higher price. Larger versions of the children and dogs groups could fetch almost double the price at auction.*

Length 4¾in/12cm £C

Various dogs

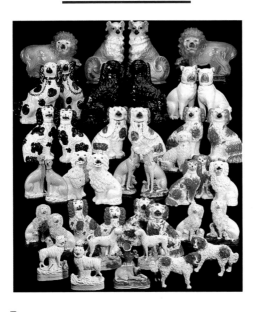

PAIRS OF DOGS AND OTHER ANIMALS, FACING LEFT
to right, are typical of the mid- to late 19th century.
Standard "comforter" spaniels, seated on their
haunches, were produced in large quantities, which
is reflected in their low value. The even less-valuable
lions and collies in the top row have glass eyes,
illustrating how the format changed c.1900.

RARER FIGURES, FOR EXAMPLE THE SPANIELS WITH THE
baskets of flowers in their mouths, fetch a higher
price. Similarly, the models of "Billy the Rat
Catcher" terriers (bottom left) are highly valued.
Poodles and greyhounds are also popular.
The St. Bernards (bottom right) command a high
price; they are probably sought after by both
Staffordshire collectors and dog breeders.

Height tallest pair 12½in/31.5cm   £A–D

Pipe-smoking spaniels

AN AMUSING VARIATION ON THE SUBJECT OF *dogs is this mid-19th century pair of pipe-smoking spaniels. While there are thousands of standard pairs of spaniels, pipe-smoking spaniels are much rarer, and this is reflected in their value.*

CARE SHOULD BE TAKEN WHEN BUYING SPANIELS OF THIS *type: the pipes are fragile and often damaged or missing, having been knocked off. On many pairs, the pipes are not the original or have been restored in some way, reducing the value of the pieces. It is better to have a figure with a few flaws than one that is poorly restored. The almost pristine condition of this pair is reflected in the price.*

Height 8½in/21.5cm £E

The pipes extend from the side of the mouth. Those on this pair have survived well, suffering only from hairline cracks.

Welsh springer spaniel

SOMETIMES KNOWN AS "ON THE SCENT", THIS
rare Parr-type Welsh springer spaniel c.1860–70 is
posed in a working position. The sport of shooting
has changed since the 19th century, and the
dogs then probably worked differently to their
modern counterparts. In a shooting party, springer
spaniels worked in front, flushing the game
before the gun. Other dogs pointed at the game,
with the nose, body and tail in a straight line,
hence the name pointer. Yet others set, or turned in
the direction of, the game, earning the name
setter. Welsh springer spaniels were also used to
retrieve game after it had been shot.

THE FIGURE SUFFERS FROM A COMMON FLAW ASSOCIATED
with overglaze enamel decoration. Because
there is no protective glaze, the pieces are
susceptible to damage from blows and as a result
flaking is common. The value of a figure
is often related to the level of flaking, but the
rarity of the piece is also a factor.

Length 10in/25cm £D

Spaniels & pups

AN ADULT SITS OVER A RECUMBENT PUPPY IN EACH
*of the spaniel groups in this pair. This is a pleasing
variation on the spaniel theme: depicting the puppies
with the adults and the fact that they are posed on
blue enamel bases seem to increase their value.
It is amusing to note that the decoration raises a
question about the parentage of the puppies, which
are marked in black patches rather than the
brown ones of the adults. Otherwise, the decoration
for these mid-19th century spaniels is standard;
they are painted in overglaze enamels.*

AN INTERESTING FEATURE IS THE HIGH DEFINITION OF THE
*animals' hair. This pair was probably produced in a
reasonably new mould. Typically, the moulds for
making figures are used often over a period of
time. Eventually, the moulds wear, so later pieces
lack some of the definition of earlier ones.*

Height 8in/20cm £D

Greyhounds

A PERENNIAL FAVOURITE, GREYHOUNDS WERE
*produced in a variety of styles. For example, the
greyhound above is holding a hare and the figure
below has an aperture in the base to be
used as a pen-holder. These models are only two
of a number made c.1860 and later.*

*T*HE GREYHOUND WAS A WORKING MAN'S DOG. TO HELP
*supplement his pot, the dog was used for poaching
or coursing on common land to catch rabbits
and hares. The 19th-century working man was
badly paid, so any food caught
in this way was a welcome addition
to the larder. This perhaps explains
why there are so many Staffordshire
models of this subject, yet few
made by more exclusive
porcelain manufacturers.*

Height greyhound with hare
7¾in/19.5cm   £B–C

Pair of cats

THESE CATS, SITTING ON THEIR HAUNCHES AND *facing left and right, are decorated with liver spots. A red enamel line encircles each base. The pair was probably manufactured in the second half of the 19th century. Dogs were more popular than cats at the time, probably because they had been appreciated as household pets for many centuries. Cats, by contrast, were often semi-feral, and until the late 19th century they were still regarded with wariness as a result of medieval superstitions.*
THE RARITY OF GENUINE 19TH-CENTURY FIGURES OF CATS IS *reflected in their value. Today, cats are extremely popular, and even later copies of cats in the Staffordshire style are saleable and sometimes appear at auction (but they should not be dated). When buying a piece, take care to ensure that a later piece is not mistaken for an earlier one.*

Height 4in/10cm £B

Two pug figures

*I*T IS UNUSUAL TO FIND PUG DOGS DEPICTED
*in Staffordshire figures from the mid-19th
century. Their lack of popularity may be because
they were typically the pets of fashionable
wealthy women and were not owned by the type
of people who bought Staffordshire pieces.
Figures of pugs began to appear by the last quarter
of the 19th century, however, and continued
into the 20th century.*

*T*HE DOGS IN THIS LATE 19TH-CENTURY PAIR ARE STANDING
*on rocky, gilt-lined bases. These pugs may have
been influenced by pieces from the German Meissen
factory, where porcelain models of pugs had
been popular since the mid-18th century.
They are good examples – in the period in which
they were made pugs were usually not as well
modelled or coloured, but were quite crude as,
indeed, are most other Staffordshire figures.*

Height 8½in/21.5cm   £D

Elephant spills

THESE CIRCUS ELEPHANTS, DRAPED WITH ORANGE and green caparisons, or coverings, were produced c.1860 as spill vases. Elephants are an unusual subject for most potters and, consequently, much sought after by collectors. Their relative rarity may be a reflection of the fact that touring menageries that owned elephants did not appear until the early 19th century.

RARITY IS NOT THE ONLY REASON THAT ELEPHANTS command high prices. The symbol of the Republican Party in the United States is an elephant, and Staffordshire figures of this kind are highly prized in that country. Elephants have been reproduced in the 20th century, and these figures are also collectable. If an early figure is desired, care should be taken to purchase one from a reputable dealer – skill is required to ascertain a piece's date.

Height 6in/15cm £D

Two pairs of cats

*T*HE BLACK-GLAZED CATS IN THIS PAIR ARE
*seated with their tails curled around them and bows
tied around their necks. They have alert
expressions and green glass eyes. Animal groups
of this period, c.1900, often have glass eyes – this
is nearly always an indication of a late date
of manufacture. Not all Staffordshire-type figures
were made in the Potteries. These were
made by Charles W. McNay and Sons at the
Bridgeness Pottery, Bo'ness, Scotland.*
Height black cats 12½in/31.5cm £B

*T*HE PAIR OF GINGER KITTENS, MODELLED LEFT AND RIGHT,
*were designed with their mouths open and
their forepaws apart from their
bodies. Like the cats above,
the kittens were produced at
a comparatively late date,
c.1900 – this reflects the
greater popularity that cat
subjects enjoyed at the
end of the 19th century.*
Height kittens 7¾in/19.5cm £B

Bo'ness horses

THESE REARING POTTERY HORSES WERE PRODUCED
c.1900 in Bo'ness, Scotland. They were painted
in shades of grey glaze, with hints of brown.
The modelling of the horses is much cruder
than that of typical mid-19th century Staffordshire
groups. The horses' hooves appear clumsily
attached to the rock, giving the impression
that they are galloping through treacle. One
assumption is that the drop in quality indicates the
need to continue making these figures at
a reasonable price, despite the vastly increased
costs of manufacturing figures at the
beginning of the 20th century.

THE HORSES HAVE A COMPARATIVELY HIGH VALUE,
given that they are late Staffordshire models
and the workmanship is crude. However,
there is a strong collectors' base for this Scottish
work and, of course, horses are as popular
today as they have always been.

Height 6in/15cm   £B

Jumbo

A SIMPLE FIGURE *of the renowned 19th-century circus elephant Jumbo sits on a round base. Jumbo was a famous beast who toured the country to popular acclaim until he became too large to handle. In 1882 he was sold by the Fellows of the Royal Zoological Society to the American showman, Phineas T. Barnum, who wanted to take him to the United States.*

A PUBLIC OUTCRY LED TO AN APPLICATION FOR A HIGH COURT *injunction, and Jumbo himself, perhaps reluctant to disappoint his British fans, refused to board the ship. Only cold and hunger eventually drove him aboard the specially adapted* Assyrian Queen. *His career in the United States was short-lived, however. In 1885 Jumbo was killed when charging – and, indeed, de-railing – an oncoming train.*

THIS FIGURE SHOULD DATE FROM 1882 TO 1885. JUMBO was, presumably, reproduced into the 20th century. Although a simple piece – with little to break off – and of a later period, Jumbo is relatively rare.

Height 6½in/16.5cm £B

Sheep shearer

THIS PORCELAIN FIGURE of a sheep shearer is an unusual agricultural subject for the period c.1840. It is well modelled, showing high definition and exceptional quality in the gilding and enamel decoration. Due to its rarity, the figure could fetch a higher price than expected at auction.

BECAUSE THE SHEEP shearer is made of porcelain, it is likely that it was produced by one of the larger Staffordshire manufacturers who made better-quality wares. For a mid-19th century piece, this figure shows greater attention to detail than usual, and this is also an indication that it was produced by a larger manufacturer. For example, extruded clay was used for the sheep's wool, much care was taken in modelling the facial features, and the decoration was applied more neatly than on standard Staffordshire figures.

Height 6in/15cm £B

This lustrous gilding is the result of using a medium of honey or water, rather than the drab and less durable mercury gilding used later.

Punch & Judy

Designed as a pair, Punch and Judy are seated on goats, facing inward. The figures are easy to identify because they are wearing costumes associated with the characters.

The models were made c.1850 using moulds only, with the exception of the extruded clay additions to decorate the goats. These particular figures represent a rarer type of the standard genre of people seated on goats. More typically, the goats were rendered with children – often the Prince of Wales and the Princess Royal. Because the children are more common and appear more frequently at auction, they generally realize only a sixth of the value of Punch and Judy, depending on their size and condition.

Height 6¾in/17cm £C

Death of the Lion Queen

THE ACTRESS ELLEN BRIGHT *was the subject for the figure "Death of the Lion Queen", made c.1850. She was the niece of the circus owner George Wombwell and became a lion queen at the tender age of 16. During her working life, Ellen appeared before Queen Victoria and other notable members of society. In 1850, however, while performing with a caged lion and tiger at Chatham in Kent, Ellen was attacked by the tiger, which seized her by the throat and killed her. The affair caused quite a sensation at the time and, ultimately, led to the prohibition of women working with dangerous wild animals, although many circuses continued to have lion kings.*

IN THIS FIGURE ELLEN IS POSING WITH WHAT APPEARS TO *be a leopard, not a tiger, playfully leaping at her in an unconvincing manner, apparently more ready to lick than bite her. Although this figure is charming, and a lion is at her side, it is not a very realistic portrayal of Ellen's fate.*

Height 14½in/37cm £C

Llywelyn's Baby

A WATCH-HOLDER GROUP WAS DESIGNED TO
*be a safe place to store a pocket watch overnight.
The watch sits in a hollow cup behind the
opening at the top, appearing for all the world
like a clock set in a pottery case.*

THIS GROUP OF PRINCE LLYWELYN'S SON AND GELERT
*was produced in the mid-19th century. It illustrates
the tragic story of the prince's dog, Gelert.
Llywelyn returned from hunting one day to find his
dog covered in blood. He immediately checked
his son's cot and was horrified to find it empty and
smeared with blood. Enraged, he drove his
sword into Gelert's side, killing him. As the dog let
out a dying howl, the child's cry could be heard
nearby; a mauled wolf was found dead in
the vicinity. Gelert had saved the child's life.
Llywelyn was so upset by his tragic mistake, he
was reputed never to have smiled again.*

Height 10½in/26.5cm   £B

Lady Isabel Burton

THIS FIGURE OF LADY ISABEL BURTON, MADE
*c.1861, shows her sitting on a camel. She was the
wife of Sir Richard Burton, a well-known
mid-19th century traveller and explorer, and she
accompanied him on several of his travels.*
AT THE TIME, IT WAS EXCEPTIONAL FOR ANY WOMAN TO
*undertake the type of travelling and activities
enjoyed by the couple. One notable exception
was Lady Hester Stanhope, who was unmarried and
had been housekeeper to her uncle William Pitt.
She not only travelled widely, but – scandalously – did
so accompanied only by her doctor. Figures were
made of both women, mounted on camels. They
are usually difficult to tell apart and, indeed,
the presence of Dr. Meryon with Lady Hester is
often the only way of identifying her.*
Height 8in/20cm £C

The Tiger Hunter

A MAN SITS ON AN ELEPHANT, WITH A TIGER BY HIS side, in this group known as "The Tiger Hunter". This is a late example of an elephant group, dated c.1900. The figure looks as though it should have an interesting story attached to it but, as far as is known, no such story has come to light.

PARTICULAR NOTE SHOULD BE TAKEN OF THE RELATIVELY crude moulding of the piece for the period. It was probably made from a single mould and so lacks some of the definition and vivacity of pieces by such potters as Sherratt, which were typically made in several stages. Elephant groups, including many 20th-century pieces, are popular at auction. A group offered at a lower price than the one suggested may be a more recent version of its late 19th-century counterparts.

Height 8½in/21.5cm   £C

Equestrian groups

VICTOR EMMANUEL II, KING OF SARDINIA AND FIRST
king of Italy (left), and Giuseppe Garibaldi
(right) feature in this pair of Parr-type equestrian
groups. They were modelled c.1861 from an
engraving in the Illustrated London News of
29 December 1860. Both men are turned in the
saddle, and their horses face each other on rocky
moulded bases, which bear titles. In 1861, Garibaldi
was instrumental in bringing Victor Emmanuel to
the Italian throne. Garibaldi visited England,
where he was a popular figure, in 1864.

THOMAS PARR WORKED IN BURSLEM BETWEEN 1852 AND
1870. This is at the beginning of a period in
which a generic grouping of potters made wares
that are referred to as "Kent and Parr-type",
and it continued until the Kent factory closed
in 1962. The work of these potters is identifiable
by their use of pale shades of enamels.

Height 15¼in/39cm £D

Crimean War figures

SULTAN

TURKEY ENGLAND FRANCE

A DEGREE OF RUSSO-PHOBIA IN THE MID-19TH
century made figures associated with the Crimean War
popular subjects. Since 1815, Great Britain
had lived through a period of comparative peace and,
no doubt, public imagination was fired by military
acts on Russia's southern border. The sultan
of Turkey, Abdul-medjid (left), and the group of three
figures symbolizing Turkey, England and France
were both made c.1854. The three allied
nations are represented by the sultan, Queen
Victoria and Napoleon III. The figure of the sultan
is comparatively rare but figures of British
and French generals abound.

THE DECORATION ON THE FIGURES IS CHARACTERISTIC
of the mid-19th century period. Few colours
were used, and blue was the predominant one. The
figures stand on gilt-lined and gilt-titled bases.

Height sultan 13in/33cm £B
Height allies 10in/25cm £B

Victoria & Albert

ALTHOUGH NOT A MATCHED PAIR, THE FIGURES ARE
of Queen Victoria and Prince Albert. The bodies
are made of a porcellaneous material associated with
many figures of the 1840s. The pieces are decorated
to a comparatively high standard and enriched
with gilding. The ermine lining of Queen Victoria's
cloak was achieved by applying extruded clay;
the same technique was used to fashion foliage
on cottage pastille-burners (see p.71).
QUEEN VICTORIA AND HER CONSORT WERE POPULAR AT THE
beginning of her reign (1837–1901). Her popularity
explains why there are, possibly, more models of
the royal couple than of any other Staffordshire
portrait figures of the mid-19th century. At the time,
these were probably comparatively expensive pieces.
Height Prince Albert 7½in/19cm   £A each

Figure of a man & girl

A MAN IN MILITARY *uniform holds a bird in one hand while supporting a child with the other in this group. The child is balancing on one leg on a cushion placed on a plinth. She seems to be holding a bunch of grapes over her head – although the man may be holding them instead. This is a difficult group to identify with a subject with certainty. It is a mid-19th century piece and could be an unidentified theatrical group or, perhaps, Prince Albert and the Princess Royal. There are hundreds of figures and groups that cover both royal and theatrical topics and not all of these have been identified.*

*T*HIS GROUP HAS A REASONABLY HIGH DEGREE OF *decoration. Although comparatively rare, many portrait groups similar to this one have dropped in value, largely because many collectors now prefer animals.*

Height 9¼in/23.5cm £A–B

Actors

THE ACTORS IN THIS RARE FIGURE GROUP OF
c.1852 are probably playing the roles of Romeo
and Juliet, but in broadly contemporary dress. This
group is similar to the one of the actresses,
and sisters, Charlotte and Susan Cushman cast in
the same roles (see p.11). While an engraving exists
of the two sisters, no evidence has yet
come to light to identify the actors on which
this particular piece was modelled.
IT WAS COMMON FOR STAFFORDSHIRE POTTERS TO COPY
engravings advertising plays and operas and,
as a result, many of these pieces can be fairly readily
identified. An added bonus is that the engravings
make it easy to date the groups, particularly if the
play had a comparatively short run.

Height 11¼in/28.5cm £B

Falconer

DESPITE CONSIDERABLE RESEARCH, the identity of many Staffordshire figures remains a mystery. This piece, however, has been identified as a falconer with a falcon perched on his hand and game birds in a basket. It could represent a theatrical source, as many other figures do, but it may simply be a falconer.

THE MID-19TH century piece is richly coloured in overglaze enamels, which have survived well. This is particularly evident in the blue dress, which does not display any of the crazing that is often seen in other enamels. The blue enamel will eventually deteriorate, but it seems to stand the test of time far better than any other colour.

FIGURES MOULDED AS A BLOCK, SUCH AS THIS ONE, ARE fairly durable. When purchasing a piece, however, take care to ensure that any extremities, such as the bird on this figure, have not been restored – these areas are much more susceptible to damage.

Height 10¼in/26cm £A

Signing the Magna Carta

In this mid-19th century group, King John is signing the Magna Carta, the basis of the English constitution. This group is a highly coloured version of the subject; they were more often sparsely or partially coloured.

This model was constructed by the Victorian process of press-moulding. To preserve the original, a working mould was created: the front and back pieces of the master mould were pressed together and the hollow filled with liquid plaster of Paris. Each working mould could be used to make several hundred figures without serious deterioration. To make the piece itself, flat sheets of damp clay were laid on to the moulds, which were pressed together, to be fired and enamelled later.

Height 13in/33cm £B

Greenwich Pensioner

THIS UNUSUAL FIGURE, ALSO KNOWN AS "THE
Amputee", is of a disabled Greenwich pensioner, who
is wearing a tricorn hat, blue jacket and orange
breeches and sitting on a sledge. It was made c.1854.
THE ROYAL HOSPITAL, GREENWICH, FIRST RECEIVED PENSIONERS,
all of whom were retired seamen, in 1705 (the
Royal Hospital in Chelsea was for army pensioners).
Although retired, Greenwich pensioners
were still obliged to wear a uniform – the blue
jacket and the hat shown here – and the hospital had
strict rules about conduct both within and
outside the grounds. All working seamen had sixpence
a month docked from their wages to contribute
to the upkeep of the institution.

Length 3in/7.5cm   £C

Cricketers & other figures

A RARE PAIR OF CRICKETERS *(TOP LEFT AND right), made c.1865, is among this interesting range of figures. An excellent example of sporting pieces, they are popular collectors' items outside the circle of Staffordshire figure collectors and appeal especially to cricket fans. Their value is about four times greater than the range given below.*

*O*THER FIGURES INCLUDE THOSE OF *S*PANIARDS *(centre left and right) and the figures of a shepherd and shepherdess (bottom left and right); they have the impressed mark "Lloyd of Shelton". Each of these groups was made c.1845.*

Height Cricketers 13¾in/35cm £C each pair

Pugilists

THE PUGILISTS JOHN CARMEL *Heenan and Tom Sayers are shown in this group c.1860. Heenan was a celebrated American boxer, Sayers the English champion. They fought the most famous boxing match of the 19th century on 17 April 1860. The fight lasted more than two hours, with neither party knocking the other out and, in the end, both men were declared champion.*

MOST REMARKABLE WAS THE FACT THAT SAYERS WAS A *middleweight boxer, whereas Heenan was not only a heavyweight but also substantially taller and heavier. In the fourth round, Sayers dislocated his right arm and was only able to survive the rest of the match by using his exceptionally skilful footwork and agility.*

IN THE 19TH CENTURY, BOXING WAS A DIFFERENT SPORT *to what it is today. It was practised by commoners and the gentry alike, using bare fists, lightly bound. Points were not awarded and there was no official limit to the number of rounds, hence the unresolved end of the Heenan–Sayers match.*

Height 9¼in/23.5cm £C

Highlander spill vase

THIS HIGHLAND *sportsman, with his hound, is well decorated in coloured enamels. He is holding a shotgun and has a pheasant at his feet. Beside him is a spill vase modelled as a tree trunk. There are many variations on the theme of Highlanders and this 19th-century figure is but one example.*

QUEEN VICTORIA AND *Prince Albert had popularized Scotland, choosing to build Balmoral Castle there, and the works of such Scottish novelists as Sir Walter Scott also contributed to this trend. After the last Jacobite rising of 1745, the wearing of tartan was prohibited to weaken the Scottish clan system. However, Victoria and Albert both wore the Stuart tartan during the Queen's reign.*

Height 13in/33cm   £B

Swirls of finely painted hair around the liver spots on the dog make the animal's coat look more realistic.

Smith & Collier

AT FIRST GLANCE, THIS GROUP OF C.1866 MAY
look like men greeting each other but, in fact, it is a
murder group. In 1866 Staffordshire farmer Thomas
Smith caught William Collier, a neighbour, poaching
on his land. Collier had already used one barrel
from his shotgun to kill rabbits, but used the second
to shoot Smith. He did not kill his victim, so he
bludgeoned Smith to death with the butt of the gun.
Collier was the last man hanged in public at Stafford
jail; the hanging was not a quick one, and it was
decided to execute prisoners in private thereafter.
THE MODEL IS NOT STRICTLY TRUE TO THE STORY, SINCE SMITH
appears to be standing up to Collier, engaging
in a fight. Doubtless, the fact that the
crime was committed in Staffordshire made it
particularly interesting to potters in the area.

Height 12¾in/32.5cm £B

Rush & Sandford

James B Rush   *Emily Sandford*

*JAMES BLOOMFIELD RUSH AND EMILY SANDFORD
are the figures in this pair. Rush owned Potash Farm
(opposite), on which he had raised a mortgage
from Isaac Jermy. Since Rush was unable to repay
the debt, Jermy foreclosed and notice was served for
30 November 1848. On 28 November, however,
Rush went to Jermy's house, shot and killed Jermy
and his son and wounded Jermy's daughter-in-law
and a servant. He conducted his own trial
defence and Emily Sandford, Rush's lover, gave most
of the evidence that convicted him. The manuscript
she carries probably represents the forgery
she knew Rush had made in an attempt to show
that Jermy had waived the debt.*

*THE HIGH VALUE OF THIS PAIR OF MURDER FIGURES, OF
c.1849, reflects the relative rarity of these
subjects and the general interest of the story.*

Height Rush 10¼in/26cm   £D

Potash Farm

Potash Farm

THIS IS A MID-19TH CENTURY MODEL OF POTASH
*Farm in Norfolk, where James Rush and his lover
Emily Sandford lived and on which the mortgage that
led to murder was secured (see opposite). Models of
celebrated buildings were a popular alternative
to those of the human protagonists, and those with
the title of the house, such as this, are more unusual
than the general ones on the market. Stanfield
Hall, where Rush committed the murders, has also
been made by Staffordshire potters.*

MODELS THAT WERE NOT PURELY DECORATIVE WERE USED AS
*moneyboxes or pastille-burners (to alleviate noxious
odours). The houses are often sparsely coloured
in gilt, but they are frequently encrusted with flowers
or extruded clay foliage at the gables.*

Length 9in/23cm £B

Church of St. Roch

*THIS MODEL OF THE CHURCH OF ST. ROCH SHOWS
an unusual building. It has two towers on either
side of a central portico, which is surmounted by
a figure of St. Roch, with his staff and his dog. St.
Roch is the patron saint of plague victims and is
almost invariably shown with a dog.*

*THE CHURCH DOES NOT APPEAR TO HAVE BEEN MODELLED
on an existing building and does not look like a
typically British church, making the subject an
unusual Stafford piece. There is, however, a church
dedicated to St. Roch in Paris, where Napoleon
Bonaparte's troops fired upon rebels on 5 October
1795. This mid-19th century example is
probably as large as any model of a building
would ever have been; most of the pastille-burners
and cottages are considerably smaller.*

Height 10in/25cm £A

Military figures

Napoleon Bonaparte (left) was popular with
the British public both during and after his lifetime,
despite waging war against Great Britain
in the late 18th to early 19th centuries. Many of the
journals of soldiers and sailors refer with
some affection to "Boney". There are numerous
Napoleon figures, and many are taken
from lithographs after works of the great painters.
This mid-19th century figure may have
been modelled from such a source.

Height 9¾in/25cm £B

Nelson (right) was also extremely popular, having
made the ultimate sacrifice for his country in 1805,
and has lived on in the public imagination since.
In this mid-19th century "Death of Nelson"
group, the admiral is seen at the moment he was
shot, supported by two seamen.

Height 8¾in/22cm £B

Equestrian generals

THOUGHT TO BE A PRUSSIAN GENERAL, THE FIGURE
*on the left dates from c.1870, the time of the
Franco–Prussian war. Although only partially
decorated, it nonetheless represents a high level
of decoration for such equestrian figures. The black
enamels show signs of deterioration, a common
occurrence in Victorian portrait figures.*

Height 11½in/29cm   £A

THE OTHER FIGURE, MADE IN 1857, IS THAT OF GENERAL SIR
*Henry Havelock. Sir Henry joined the army shortly
after the Battle of Waterloo, served most of his
career in India and Afghanistan and was a hero of the
Indian Mutiny, relieving Lucknow in 1857. He was
created a Knight Commander of the Bath as a
consequence but died shortly afterward. The base
of such figures is often titled with the general's name,
since many of these figures are similar.*

Height 8¾in/22cm   £A

King of Prussia

THIS FIGURE OF **K**ING **W**ILLIAM **I** *of Prussia on horseback was probably made by Samson Smith c.1870. This particular piece has been heavily restored – and not very well. Restoration does not always last indefinitely, and sometimes only for 20 years. The age of this restoration is beginning to show: the restored areas have started to discolour – for example, the neck of the horse has turned yellow.*

OTHER AREAS OF THE FIGURE WERE ALSO RESTORED, MAKING *it a good example to study to see where restoration has been done. The King's head has been broken off and reattached to the neck. The base has been damaged and most of the gilt title repainted with gold paint instead of gilt. Other areas of gilt have also been touched up with gold paint, most noticeably the horse's bridle.*

Height 15in/38cm under £A

Fine cracks in glaze, known as crazing, can be caused by shrinkage. Crazing occurs more often in light colours.

Edward VII

MODELLED HOLDING HIS HAT, this figure of Edward VII was made c.1901. It is typical of pieces made at the end of the late 19th century, a period in which Staffordshire manufacturers continued to produce a huge volume of figures. The production of Staffordshire figures began to dwindle in the early 20th century, perhaps because there was no demand for such pieces. For Queen Elizabeth's coronation in 1952 and jubilee in 1977, hundreds of commemorative pieces were produced, but they were printed mugs rather than decorative figures.

THIS FIGURE IS COMPARATIVELY UNUSUAL IN THAT IT IS quite highly decorated for the period. If end-of-the-century Staffordshire figures have anything in common, it is that they are almost universally sparsely decorated.

Height 12in/30cm £A

Reproductions

Copies of figures made in the 19th century
and earlier are still being manufactured today, most
notably in the Far East. A well-known factory,
William Kent Ltd. of Burslem continued until
1962 to manufacture figures that they had produced
earlier. This figure is similar to No. 277, which
was featured in their catalogue of the mid-1950s.
The 20th-century Kent pieces would
not necessarily be termed "fake" because – with
the exception of World War II – production of
these figures had not been interrupted.

Such reproduction figures are seldom sold in
specialist Staffordshire figure sales, since they detract
from genuine pieces in the sale. These pieces
can be bought inexpensively, however, at small
auction houses and through the trade.

Height 9in/23cm £A

Glossary

BISCUIT A piece of pottery after the first firing, before it is glazed.

BOCAGE The flower-encrusted bushes or trees seen behind some figures; from the French (thicket).

BODY The mixture of raw materials from which pottery is made.

CRAZING The fine lines or cracks that appear on a glaze, which occurs when the body and the glaze shrink at different rates as they cool after a firing.

CREAMWARE A cream-coloured earthenware, or porous pottery, with a clear lead glaze.

ENAMEL A type of smooth paint for decorating ceramics, made of powdered glass, tinted with metallic oxides and mixed with an oil medium. It is painted on the piece, which is then fired.

FAMILY Literally, a group of potters from the same family.

FIRING The "cooking" of the pottery, glazes and enamels in a kiln to harden the body or fix the decoration to it.

FLATBACK A figure designed to be seen from the front; the back is unmodelled, or flat.

GILDING Gold paint applied to figures. It was originally applied with an oil, water or honey medium; later, it was applied with a mercury amalgam.

GLAZE A glass-based coating, often decorative, applied to biscuit as a sealant against moisture.

GROUP A piece consisting of more than one figure.

KILN A specially constructed oven, in which the biscuit and decoration are fired.

OVERGLAZE The process by which glaze is applied over the top of a glazed biscuit piece.

PARR-TYPE Wares in the style of the Parr factory (see p.39).

PEARLWARE A blue-tinted glaze applied to the body, possibly in imitation of porcelain; achieved by adding cobalt.

PORCELAIN A thin, hard-fired ware, which is translucent when held to the light and more delicate than pottery. Until the 19th century, only a few manufacturers made it.

PORCELLANEOUS A hard-fired fine stone china made in imitation of porcelain but without the translucent effect.

PRESS-MOULD Where sheets of clay are pressed into two halves of a mould, which are brought together to make a figure.

PRATT-GLAZE A ware coloured with glazes similar to ones used by the Pratt family (see p.16).

SALTGLAZE A thin, clear glaze created when salt is thrown into the kiln and vaporizes.

SLIP MOULD A single mould into which liquid clay is poured, allowed to dry, then turned out.

SPILL VASE A decorative piece designed to hold spills for lighting fires or pipes.

WOOD-TYPE A ware similar to ones made by the Wood family, but unmarked (see p.21).

Index

Acknowledgments

All pictures courtesy of Christie's South Kensington
except for the following:
Christie's Images: 7, 13–15, 34, 36.
City Museum & Art Gallery, Stoke-on-Trent/E.T. Archive: 10.
City Museum & Art Gallery, Stoke-on-Trent: 8–9.
Garrick Club/E.T. Archive: 11.
Victoria & Albert Museum: 6, 12.
Illustrators: **Lorraine Harrison** (borders), **Debbie Hinks** (endpapers).